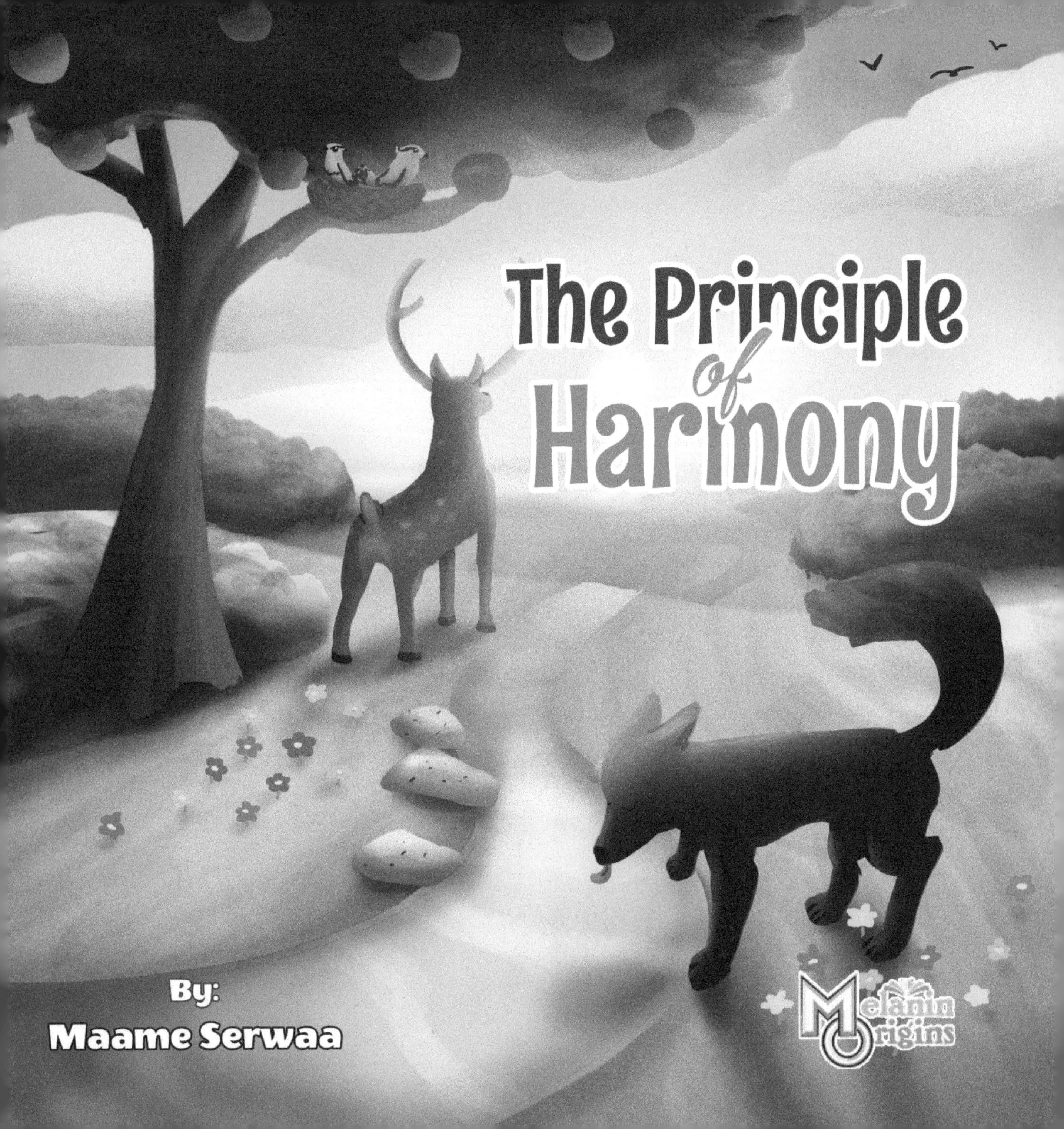
The Principle
of
Harmony
By:
Maame Serwaa
Melanin Origins

Published by Melanin Origins

PO Box 122123; Arlington, TX 76012

First Edition

Library of Congress Control Number: 2021942095

ISBN: 978-1-62676-522-1 hardback

ISBN: 978-1-62676-523-8 paperback

ISBN: 978-1-62676-524-5 ebook

The Principle of Harmony

"Life is complimentary; one to another. I will strive to always make the right decisions & be in rhythm with what is good for myself, my family, and the world."

MA'AT SERIES

www.MelaninOrigins.com

Take a look around and watch the world dance.

Every motion, every breath, and every being compliments each other. This is harmony.

Harmony teaches us the beauty of being ourselves.

It shows us that we are unique and gives us strength beyond our imagination.

From the plants and the trees, to the air and the sky,

From people and animals,
to the sun and moon;

Everything has a purpose and a role to play.

As you do your part and as I do mine... the world will continue to dance, in harmony.

Thousands of years ago, as the legend states, Ma'at gave the world a simple guide to remind us of what matters the most.

Ma'at
1. TRUTH: based in fact with honesty and integrity.
2. JUSTICE: a state of fairness and lawful judgment.
3. RIGHTEOUSNESS: a state of consistent good conduct.
4. RECIPROCITY: "What goes around comes around."
5. BALANCE: an equal distribution of weight.
6. ORDER: the correct sequence of thought and action.
7. HARMONY: One accord; a pleasing arrangement.

Ma'at reminds us that we are here
to be the best we can possibly be,

And we can achieve any and every thing our heart desires by staying true to who we are.

Whether we are happy or sad, we should never stop believing in the heights we can reach.

Allow purpose to be your guide and you will see the beauty of harmony in the things you do.

We are all pieces of one giant puzzle.

Our ancestors laid out the perfect map with principles to help us navigate this giant world.

Let's always serve our purpose to make the world a better place and show others the true beauty of harmony.

Take a look around and watch the world dance.

Modern Day Melanin Origins

This book is dedicated to the one and only beloved Dr. Joy DeGruy.

Dr. Joy DeGruy is a nationally and internationally renowned educator with research focused on the intersection of racism, trauma, violence, and American chattel slavery. She is most known for her book "Post Traumatic Slave Syndrome: America's Legacy of Enduring Injury & Healing", originally published by UpTone Press in 2005.

DeGruy and her research projects have been featured in news and activist coverage of contemporary African-American social issues, in addition to public lectures and workshops on U.S. college campuses.

www.JoyDeGruy.com

CPSIA information can be obtained
at www.ICGtesting.com
Printed in the USA
LVHW070729270322
714271LV00040B/180

9 781626 765221